Ramadan Journal

30 days of prayer, fasting and reflection

Published by LeNoble Publishing

Copyright ©2021

ISBN: 978-1-955132-09-1

This Journal Belongs To:

_____

Calendar

Sunday	Monday	Tuesday	Wednesday

Calendar

Thursday	Friday	Saturday	Notes

Reading Log

Day يوم	Juz جز	From Ayaat من آيات	To Ayaat لآيات

Reading Log

Day يوم	Juz جز	From Ayaat من آيات	To Ayaat لآيات

رمضان 1

Date/ خيرات: _____

☐ Fajr — صلاة الفجر   ☐ Dhuhr — صَلَاة الظهر

☐ Asr — صلاة العصر   ☐ Maghrib — صلاة المغرب

☐ Isha'a — صلاة العشاء   ☐ Taraweeh — تراويح

☐ Reading completed for today — اكتملت القراءة لهذا اليوم

Ayaah/Hadith for Today
آية/ حديث اليوم

_____

_____

_____

My Goals
أهدافي

_____

_____

_____

Things to Do
الأشياء الذي ينبغي فعلها

_____

_____

_____

_____

_____

My Good Deeds
أعمالي الصالحة

_____

_____

_____

_____

Meals
وجبات

Iftar
الإفطار

Suhoor
سحور

_____

_____

_____

_____

_____

Water Tracker
تعقب المياه

(1) (2) (3) (4) (5) (6) (7) (8)

Daily Reflection
تفكر و تدبر

How did my day go? What would I like to achieve/do this month?

_____

_____

_____

_____

_____

_____

_____

_____

_____

رمضان 2

Date/خيرات: _____

- ☐ Fajr — صلاة الفجر
- ☐ Asr — صلاة العصر
- ☐ Isha'a — صلاة العشاء
- ☐ Reading completed for today — اكتملت القراءة لهذا اليوم

- ☐ Dhuhr — صَلَاة الظهر
- ☐ Maghrib — صلاة المغرب
- ☐ Taraweeh — تراويح

Ayaah/Hadith for Today
آية/ حديث اليوم

_____

_____

_____

My Goals
أهدافي

_____

_____

_____

My Good Deeds
أعمالي الصالحة

_____

_____

_____

Things to Do
الأشياء الذي ينبغي فعلها

_____

_____

_____

_____

_____

_____

Meals
وجبات

Iftar الإفطار	**Suhoor** سحور
_____	_____
_____	_____
_____	_____
_____	_____
_____	_____

Water Tracker
تعقب المياه

(1) (2) (3) (4) (5) (6) (7) (8)

Daily Reflection
تفكر و تدبر

How did my day go? What is something I did not do last Ramadan that I want to do this year?

_____

_____

_____

_____

_____

_____

_____

_____

_____

_____

رمضان 3

Date/ خيرات: _____

- ⬜ Fajr   صلاة الفجر
- ⬜ Asr   صلاة العصر
- ⬜ Isha'a   صلاة العشاء
- ⬜ Reading completed for today   اكتملت القراءة لهذا اليوم

- ⬜ Dhuhr   صَلَاة الظهر
- ⬜ Maghrib   صلاة المغرب
- ⬜ Taraweeh   تراويح

Ayaah/Hadith for Today
آية/ حديث اليوم

_____

_____

_____

My Goals
أهدافي

_____

_____

_____

My Good Deeds
أعمالي الصالحة

_____

_____

_____

Things to Do
الأشياء الذي ينبغي فعلها

_____

_____

_____

_____

_____

_____

Meals
وجبات

Iftar
الإفطار

Suhoor
سحور

_____   _____

_____   _____

_____   _____

_____   _____

_____   _____

Water Tracker
تعقب المياه

(1) (2) (3) (4) (5) (6) (7) (8)

Daily Reflection
تفكر و تدبر

How did my day go? What is a blessing I am thankful for today?

_____

_____

_____

_____

_____

_____

_____

_____

رمضان 4

Date/ خيرات: _____

- ☐ Fajr   صلاة الفجر
- ☐ Asr   صلاة العصر
- ☐ Isha'a   صلاة العشاء
- ☐ Reading completed for today   اكتملت القراءة لهذا اليوم

- ☐ Dhuhr   صَلاة الظهر
- ☐ Maghrib   صلاة المغرب
- ☐ Taraweeh   تراويح

Ayaah/Hadith for Today
آية/ حديث اليوم

_____

_____

_____

My Goals
أهدافي

_____

_____

_____

_____

Things to Do
الأشياء الذي ينبغي فعلها

_____

_____

_____

_____

My Good Deeds
أعمالي الصالحة

_____

_____

_____

_____

Meals
وجبات

Iftar
الإفطار

Suhoor
سحور

_____   _____
_____   _____
_____   _____
_____   _____
_____   _____

Water Tracker
تعقب المياه

(1) (2) (3) (4) (5) (6) (7) (8)

Daily Reflection
تفكر و تدبر

How did my day go? What progress did I make towards my goals?

_____
_____
_____
_____
_____
_____
_____
_____
_____
_____

Sudoku #1

3	7						5	9
	1				7		6	
6			3	2	9	1	4	
5	4	7	9	6		3	2	
	2			3			8	6
	6			1	4	7		
1	5				3		7	8
			6			5		
7	3			5				

رمضان 5

Date/خيرات: ـــــــــــــــــــــ

- [ ] Fajr — صلاة الفجر
- [ ] Asr — صلاة العصر
- [ ] Isha'a — صلاة العشاء
- [ ] Reading completed for today — اكتملت القراءة لهذا اليوم

- [ ] Dhuhr — صَلَاة الظهر
- [ ] Maghrib — صلاة المغرب
- [ ] Taraweeh — تراويح

Ayaah/Hadith for Today
آية/ حديث اليوم

ـ_____

ـ_____

ـ_____

My Goals
أهدافي

ـ_____

ـ_____

ـ_____

My Good Deeds
أعمالي الصالحة

ـ_____

ـ_____

Things to Do
الأشياء الذي ينبغي فعلها

ـ_____

ـ_____

ـ_____

ـ_____

ـ_____

ـ_____

ـ_____

Meals
وجبات

Iftar
الإفطار

Suhoor
سحور

_____
_____
_____
_____
_____

Water Tracker
تعقب المياه

(1) (2) (3) (4) (5) (6) (7) (8)

Daily Reflection
تفكر و تدبر

How did my day go? What is one thing I did better today? How does that make me feel?

_____
_____
_____
_____
_____
_____
_____
_____
_____

رمضان 6

Date/خيرات: _____

- ☐ Fajr — صلاة الفجر
- ☐ Asr — صلاة العصر
- ☐ Isha'a — صلاة العشاء
- ☐ Dhuhr — صَلَاة الظهر
- ☐ Maghrib — صلاة المغرب
- ☐ Taraweeh — تراويح
- ☐ Reading completed for today — اكتملت القراءة لهذا اليوم

Ayaah/Hadith for Today
آية/ حديث اليوم

_____

_____

_____

My Goals
أهدافي

_____

_____

_____

Things to Do
الأشياء الذي ينبغي فعلها

_____

_____

_____

My Good Deeds
أعمالي الصالحة

_____

_____

_____

_____

_____

Meals
وجبات

Iftar
الإفطار

Suhoor
سحور

Water Tracker
تعقب المياه

(1) (2) (3) (4) (5) (6) (7) (8)

Daily Reflection
تفكر و تدبر

How did my day go? What is one thing I can do better tomorrow? How can I do that?

Sudoku #2

					7			
	2	7	6			5	3	
1			2	5	9		7	4
	4					2	9	
8				5			1	
	9	5		4	3	8	6	7
			3	7	6			1
	1	9	5	8				
6				9		7	8	2

رمضان 7

Date/ خيرات: _____

- ☐ Fajr   صلاة الفجر
- ☐ Asr   صلاة العصر
- ☐ Isha'a   صلاة العشاء
- ☐ Reading completed for today   اكتملت القراءة لهذا اليوم

- ☐ Dhuhr   صَلَاة الظهر
- ☐ Maghrib   صلاة المغرب
- ☐ Taraweeh   تراويح

Ayaah/Hadith for Today
آية/ حديث اليوم

_____

_____

_____

My Goals
أهدافي

_____

_____

_____

My Good Deeds
أعمالي الصالحة

_____

_____

_____

Things to Do
الأشياء الذي ينبغي فعلها

_____

_____

_____

_____

_____

_____

Meals
وجبات

Iftar
الإفطار

_____
_____
_____
_____
_____

Suhoor
سحور

_____
_____
_____
_____
_____

Water Tracker
تعقب المياه

(1) (2) (3) (4) (5) (6) (7) (8)

Daily Reflection
تفكر و تدبر

How did my day go? What is a special moment I want to remember from today?

_____
_____
_____
_____
_____
_____
_____
_____
_____

رمضان 8

Date/خيرات: _____

- [ ] Fajr   صلاة الفجر
- [ ] Asr   صلاة العصر
- [ ] Isha'a   صلاة العشاء
- [ ] Reading completed for today   اكتملت القراءة لهذا اليوم

- [ ] Dhuhr   صَلَاة الظهر
- [ ] Maghrib   صلاة المغرب
- [ ] Taraweeh   تراويح

Ayaah/Hadith for Today
آية/ حديث اليوم

_____

_____

_____

My Goals
أهدافي

_____

_____

_____

Things to Do
الأشياء الذي ينبغي فعلها

_____

_____

_____

My Good Deeds
أعمالي الصالحة

_____

_____

_____

_____

Meals
وجبات

Iftar
الإفطار

Suhoor
سحور

Water Tracker
تعقب المياه

(1) (2) (3) (4) (5) (6) (7) (8)

Daily Reflection
تفكر و تدبر

How did my day go? What is my favorite Ramadan tradition and why is it special for me?

_____

_____

_____

_____

_____

_____

_____

_____

_____

_____

_____

رمضان 9

خيرات /Date: _____

- ◯ Fajr — صلاة الفجر
- ◯ Dhuhr — صَلَاة الظهر
- ◯ Asr — صلاة العصر
- ◯ Maghrib — صلاة المغرب
- ◯ Isha'a — صلاة العشاء
- ◯ Taraweeh — تراويح
- ◯ Reading completed for today — اكتملت القراءة لهذا اليوم

Ayaah/Hadith for Today
آية/ حديث اليوم

_____

_____

_____

My Goals
أهدافي

_____

_____

_____

Things to Do
الأشياء الذي ينبغي فعلها

_____

_____

_____

My Good Deeds
أعمالي الصالحة

_____

_____

_____

_____

Meals
وجبات

Iftar	Suhoor
الإفطار	سحور

_____ _____

_____ _____

_____ _____

_____ _____

_____ _____

Water Tracker
تعقب المياه

(1) (2) (3) (4) (5) (6) (7) (8)

Daily Reflection
تفكر و تدبر

How did my day go? What is a blessing I am thankful for today?

_____

_____

_____

_____

_____

_____

_____

_____

_____

رمضان 10

Date/ خيرات: _____

- ◯ Fajr   صلاة الفجر
- ◯ Asr   صلاة العصر
- ◯ Isha'a   صلاة العشاء
- ◯ Reading completed for today   اكتملت القراءة لهذا اليوم

- ◯ Dhuhr   صَلَاة الظهر
- ◯ Maghrib   صلاة المغرب
- ◯ Taraweeh   تراويح

Ayaah/Hadith for Today
آية/ حديث اليوم

_____

_____

_____

My Goals
أهدافي

_____

_____

_____

My Good Deeds
أعمالي الصالحة

_____

_____

_____

Things to Do
الأشياء الذي ينبغي فعلها

_____

_____

_____

_____

_____

_____

_____

Meals
وجبات

Iftar
الإفطار

Suhoor
سحور

_____
_____
_____
_____
_____

_____
_____
_____
_____
_____

Water Tracker
تعقب المياه

(1) (2) (3) (4) (5) (6) (7) (8)

Daily Reflection
تفكر و تدبر

How did my day go? What progress did I make towards my goals?

_____
_____
_____
_____
_____
_____
_____
_____
_____

Sudoku #3

		7			6			9
	4	2	3		5			6
			2				3	
		8	6			9		5
5			8	2				
		3		5	7		6	
8	2	9		3	4	6	7	
	3	6		8		5		2
7	5							3

رمضان 11

Date/ خيرات: _____

- ☐ Fajr — صلاة الفجر
- ☐ Dhuhr — صَلَاة الظهر
- ☐ Asr — صلاة العصر
- ☐ Maghrib — صلاة المغرب
- ☐ Isha'a — صلاة العشاء
- ☐ Taraweeh — تراويح
- ☐ Reading completed for today — اكتملت القراءة لهذا اليوم

Ayaah/Hadith for Today
آية/ حديث اليوم

_____

_____

_____

My Goals
أهدافي

Things to Do
الأشياء الذي ينبغي فعلها

_____

_____

_____

My Good Deeds
أعمالي الصالحة

_____

_____

_____

_____

Meals
وجبات

Iftar
الإفطار

Suhoor
سحور

_____

_____

_____

_____

_____

Water Tracker
تعقب المياه

(1) (2) (3) (4) (5) (6) (7) (8)

Daily Reflection
تفكر و تدبر

How did my day go? What is one thing I did better today? How does that make me feel?

_____

_____

_____

_____

_____

_____

_____

_____

_____

رمضان 12

Date/خيارات: _____

- ⬭ Fajr — صلاة الفجر
- ⬭ Asr — صلاة العصر
- ⬭ Isha'a — صلاة العشاء
- ⬭ Dhuhr — صَلَاة الظهر
- ⬭ Maghrib — صلاة المغرب
- ⬭ Taraweeh — تراويح
- ⬭ Reading completed for today — اكتملت القراءة لهذا اليوم

Ayaah/Hadith for Today
آية/ حديث اليوم

_____

_____

_____

My Goals
أهدافي

_____

_____

_____

My Good Deeds
أعمالي الصالحة

_____

_____

_____

Things to Do
الأشياء الذي ينبغي فعلها

_____

_____

_____

_____

_____

_____

_____

Meals
وجبات

Iftar
الإفطار

Suhoor
سحور

_____   _____

_____   _____

_____   _____

_____   _____

_____   _____

Water Tracker
تعقب المياه

(1) (2) (3) (4) (5) (6) (7) (8)

Daily Reflection
تفكر و تدبر

How did my day go? What is one thing I can do better tomorrow? How can I do that?

_____

_____

_____

_____

_____

_____

_____

_____

_____

_____

Sudoku #4

1					7	3		4	
7			9	8			2	3	
9		6							
	1	2			9	6			4
			8						2
6	8		2		4			5	
	9								
3				9	7	4			8
8	6	4	3			2	1	9	7

رمضان 13

Date/ خيرات: _____

- ⬜ Fajr   صلاة الفجر
- ⬜ Asr   صلاة العصر
- ⬜ Isha'a   صلاة العشاء
- ⬜ Dhuhr   صَلَاة الظهر
- ⬜ Maghrib   صلاة المغرب
- ⬜ Taraweeh   تراويح
- ⬜ Reading completed for today   اكتملت القراءة لهذا اليوم

Ayaah/Hadith for Today
آية/ حديث اليوم

_____

_____

_____

My Goals
أهدافي

_____

_____

_____

My Good Deeds
أعمالي الصالحة

_____

_____

_____

Things to Do
الأشياء الذي ينبغي فعلها

_____

_____

_____

_____

_____

_____

_____

Meals
وجبات

Iftar
الإفطار

_____

_____

_____

_____

_____

Suhoor
سحور

_____

_____

_____

_____

_____

Water Tracker
تعقب المياه

(1) (2) (3) (4) (5) (6) (7) (8)

Daily Reflection
تفكر و تدبر

How did my day go? What is a special moment I want to remember from today?

_____

_____

_____

_____

_____

_____

_____

_____

_____

رمضان 14

Date/ خيرات: _____

- ◯ Fajr — صلاة الفجر
- ◯ Asr — صلاة العصر
- ◯ Isha'a — صلاة العشاء
- ◯ Reading completed for today — اكتملت القراءة لهذا اليوم

- ◯ Dhuhr — صَلَاة الظهر
- ◯ Maghrib — صلاة المغرب
- ◯ Taraweeh — تراويح

Ayaah/Hadith for Today
آية/ حديث اليوم

_____

_____

_____

My Goals
أهدافي

_____

_____

_____

My Good Deeds
أعمالي الصالحة

_____

_____

_____

_____

Things to Do
الأشياء الذي ينبغي فعلها

_____

_____

_____

_____

_____

_____

_____

Meals
وجبات

Iftar
الإفطار

Suhoor
سحور

_____

_____

_____

_____

_____

_____

_____

_____

_____

_____

Water Tracker
تعقب المياه

(1) (2) (3) (4) (5) (6) (7) (8)

Daily Reflection
تفكر و تدبر

How did my day go? What is a blessing I am thankful for today?

_____

_____

_____

_____

_____

_____

_____

_____

_____

_____

رمضان 15

Date/ خيرات: _____

- ☐ Fajr صلاة الفجر
- ☐ Asr صلاة العصر
- ☐ Isha'a صلاة العشاء
- ☐ Reading completed for today اكتملت القراءة لهذا اليوم

- ☐ Dhuhr صَلَاة الظهر
- ☐ Maghrib صلاة المغرب
- ☐ Taraweeh تراويح

Ayaah/Hadith for Today
آية/ حديث اليوم

_____

_____

_____

My Goals
أهدافي

_____

_____

_____

My Good Deeds
أعمالي الصالحة

_____

_____

_____

Things to Do
الأشياء الذي ينبغي فعلها

_____

_____

_____

_____

_____

_____

Meals
وجبات

Iftar
الإفطار

_____
_____
_____
_____
_____

Suhoor
سحور

_____
_____
_____
_____
_____

Water Tracker
تعقب المياه

(1) (2) (3) (4) (5) (6) (7) (8)

Daily Reflection
تفكر و تدبر

How did my day go? What progress did I make towards my goals?

_____
_____
_____
_____
_____
_____
_____
_____
_____

رمضان 16

Date/ خيرات: _____

◯ Fajr   صلاة الفجر   ◯ Dhuhr   صَلَاة الظهر

◯ Asr   صلاة العصر   ◯ Maghrib   صلاة المغرب

◯ Isha'a   صلاة العشاء   ◯ Taraweeh   تراويح

◯ Reading completed for today   اكتملت القراءة لهذا اليوم

Ayaah/Hadith for Today
آية/ حديث اليوم

_____

_____

_____

My Goals
أهدافي

_____

_____

_____

My Good Deeds
أعمالي الصالحة

_____

_____

_____

Things to Do
الأشياء الذي ينبغي فعلها

_____

_____

_____

_____

_____

_____

_____

Meals
وجبات

Iftar
الإفطار

Suhoor
سحور

_____
_____
_____
_____
_____

_____
_____
_____
_____
_____

Water Tracker
تعقب المياه

(1) (2) (3) (4) (5) (6) (7) (8)

Daily Reflection
تفكر و تدبر

How did my day go? What is one thing I did better today? How does that make me feel?

_____
_____
_____
_____
_____
_____
_____
_____
_____
_____

Sudoku #5

5			2				4	3
2	1		4			6		7
			6		3	1	2	5
8	5			9		4	6	1
3		1			6		8	2
6	7						5	9
1		5		3	4			6
			9		5			4

رمضان 17

Date/خيرات: _____

- ◯ Fajr   صلاة الفجر
- ◯ Asr   صلاة العصر
- ◯ Isha'a   صلاة العشاء
- ◯ Reading completed for today   اكتملت القراءة لهذا اليوم

- ◯ Dhuhr   صَلَاة الظهر
- ◯ Maghrib   صلاة المغرب
- ◯ Taraweeh   تراويح

Ayaah/Hadith for Today
آية/ حديث اليوم

_____
_____
_____

My Goals
أهدافي

_____
_____
_____

My Good Deeds
أعمالي الصالحة

_____
_____
_____

Things to Do
الأشياء الذي ينبغي فعلها

_____
_____
_____
_____
_____
_____
_____

Meals
وجبات

Iftar
الإفطار

Suhoor
سحور

_____
_____
_____
_____
_____

_____
_____
_____
_____
_____

Water Tracker
تعقب المياه

(1) (2) (3) (4) (5) (6) (7) (8)

Daily Reflection
تفكر و تدبر

How did my day go? What is one thing I can do better tomorrow? How can I do that?

_____
_____
_____
_____
_____
_____
_____
_____
_____
_____

رمضان 18

Date/خيرات: _____

- ☐ Fajr   صلاة الفجر
- ☐ Asr   صلاة العصر
- ☐ Isha'a   صلاة العشاء
- ☐ Reading completed for today   اكتملت القراءة لهذا اليوم

- ☐ Dhuhr   صَلَاة الظهر
- ☐ Maghrib   صلاة المغرب
- ☐ Taraweeh   تراويح

Ayaah/Hadith for Today
آية/ حديث اليوم

_____
_____
_____

My Goals
أهدافي

_____
_____
_____

My Good Deeds
أعمالي الصالحة

_____
_____
_____

Things to Do
الأشياء الذي ينبغي فعلها

_____
_____
_____
_____
_____
_____

Meals
وجبات

Iftar
الإفطار

Suhoor
سحور

_____   _____
_____   _____
_____   _____
_____   _____
_____   _____

Water Tracker
تعقب المياه

(1) (2) (3) (4) (5) (6) (7) (8)

Daily Reflection
تفكر و تدبر

How did my day go? What is a special moment I want to remember from today?

_____
_____
_____
_____
_____
_____
_____
_____
_____
_____

Sudoku #6

	7						2	5
5	3				9		7	
		1		5				
4	1		7	8		2		
				4	3	1		7
7		3	1		2			
	4	7		6				9
1		8		7		6	3	
2	6		3			7		4

رمضان 19

Date/ خيرات: _____

- ◯ Fajr — صلاة الفجر
- ◯ Asr — صلاة العصر
- ◯ Isha'a — صلاة العشاء
- ◯ Reading completed for today — اكتملت القراءة لهذا اليوم

- ◯ Dhuhr — صَلَاة الظهر
- ◯ Maghrib — صلاة المغرب
- ◯ Taraweeh — تراويح

Ayaah/Hadith for Today
آية/ حديث اليوم

_____

_____

_____

My Goals
أهدافي

_____

_____

_____

_____

My Good Deeds
أعمالي الصالحة

_____

_____

Things to Do
الأشياء الذي ينبغي فعلها

_____

_____

_____

_____

_____

_____

_____

Meals
وجبات

Iftar الإفطار	**Suhoor** سحور
_____	_____
_____	_____
_____	_____
_____	_____
_____	_____

Water Tracker
تعقب المياه

(1) (2) (3) (4) (5) (6) (7) (8)

Daily Reflection
تفكر و تدبر

How did my day go? What is a blessing I am thankful for today?

_____

_____

_____

_____

_____

_____

_____

_____

رمضان 20

Date/ خيرات: _____

- ◯ Fajr — صلاة الفجر
- ◯ Asr — صلاة العصر
- ◯ Isha'a — صلاة العشاء
- ◯ Reading completed for today — اكتملت القراءة لهذا اليوم

- ◯ Dhuhr — صَلَاة الظهر
- ◯ Maghrib — صلاة المغرب
- ◯ Taraweeh — تراويح

Ayaah/Hadith for Today
آية/ حديث اليوم

_____

_____

_____

My Goals
أهدافي

_____

_____

_____

My Good Deeds
أعمالي الصالحة

_____

_____

_____

Things to Do
الأشياء الذي ينبغي فعلها

_____

_____

_____

_____

_____

_____

Meals
وجبات

Iftar
الإفطار

Suhoor
سحور

_____
_____
_____
_____
_____

_____
_____
_____
_____
_____

Water Tracker
تعقب المياه

(1) (2) (3) (4) (5) (6) (7) (8)

Daily Reflection
تفكر و تدبر

How did my day go? What progress did I make towards my goals?

_____
_____
_____
_____
_____
_____
_____
_____
_____
_____

رمضان 21

Date/ خيرات: _____

- ☐ Fajr   صلاة الفجر
- ☐ Asr   صلاة العصر
- ☐ Isha'a   صلاة العشاء
- ☐ Reading completed for today   اكتملت القراءة لهذا اليوم

- ☐ Dhuhr   صَلَاة الظهر
- ☐ Maghrib   صلاة المغرب
- ☐ Taraweeh   تراويح

Ayaah/Hadith for Today
آية/ حديث اليوم

_____

_____

_____

My Goals
أهدافي

_____

_____

_____

Things to Do
الأشياء الذي ينبغي فعلها

_____

_____

_____

My Good Deeds
أعمالي الصالحة

_____

_____

_____

_____

_____

_____

Meals
وجبات

Iftar
الإفطار

_____
_____
_____
_____
_____

Suhoor
سحور

_____
_____
_____
_____
_____

Water Tracker
تعقب المياه

(1) (2) (3) (4) (5) (6) (7) (8)

Daily Reflection
تفكر و تدبر

How did my day go? What is one thing I did better today? How does that make me feel?

_____
_____
_____
_____
_____
_____
_____
_____
_____
_____

رمضان 22

Date/ خيرات: _____

○ Fajr   صلاة الفجر   ○ Dhuhr   صَلَاة الظهر

○ Asr   صلاة العصر   ○ Maghrib   صلاة المغرب

○ Isha'a   صلاة العشاء   ○ Taraweeh   تراويح

○ Reading completed for today   اكتملت القراءة لهذا اليوم

Ayaah/Hadith for Today
آية/ حديث اليوم

_____

_____

_____

My Goals
أهدافي

Things to Do
الأشياء الذي ينبغي فعلها

_____

_____

_____

My Good Deeds
أعمالي الصالحة

_____

_____

_____

Meals
وجبات

Iftar
الإفطار

Suhoor
سحور

_____   _____
_____   _____
_____   _____
_____   _____
_____   _____

Water Tracker
تعقب المياه

(1) (2) (3) (4) (5) (6) (7) (8)

Daily Reflection
تفكر و تدبر

How did my day go? What is one thing I can do better tomorrow? How can I do that?

_____
_____
_____
_____
_____
_____
_____
_____
_____
_____
_____

Sudoku #7

2		3			7	1		
	5	1		9			8	7
					4			
		8	2		5		7	6
6	2		7			5		
5			8		9			
1			9		8			5
	7		4				1	
		4		5	3	7	2	9

رمضان 23

Date/ خيرات: _____

◯ Fajr   صلاة الفجر   ◯ Dhuhr   صَلَاة الظهر

◯ Asr   صلاة العصر   ◯ Maghrib   صلاة المغرب

◯ Isha'a   صلاة العشاء   ◯ Taraweeh   تراويح

◯ Reading completed for today   اكتملت القراءة لهذا اليوم

Ayaah/Hadith for Today
آية/ حديث اليوم

_____

_____

_____

My Goals
أهدافي

_____

_____

_____

Things to Do
الأشياء الذي ينبغي فعلها

_____

_____

_____

_____

My Good Deeds
أعمالي الصالحة

_____

_____

_____

_____

_____

_____

Meals
وجبات

Iftar
الإفطار

_____

_____

_____

_____

_____

Suhoor
سحور

_____

_____

_____

_____

Water Tracker
تعقب المياه

(1)　(2)　(3)　(4)　(5)　(6)　(7)　(8)

Daily Reflection
تفكر و تدبر

How did my day go? What is a special moment I want to remember from today?

_____

_____

_____

_____

_____

_____

_____

_____

_____

رمضان 24

Date/ خيرات: _____

◯ Fajr   صلاة الفجر   ◯ Dhuhr   صَلَاة الظهر

◯ Asr   صلاة العصر   ◯ Maghrib   صلاة المغرب

◯ Isha'a   صلاة العشاء   ◯ Taraweeh   تراويح

◯ Reading completed for today   اكتملت القراءة لهذا اليوم

Ayaah/Hadith for Today
آية/ حديث اليوم

_____

_____

_____

My Goals
أهدافي

Things to Do
الأشياء الذي ينبغي فعلها

_____   _____

_____   _____

_____   _____

My Good Deeds
أعمالي الصالحة

_____   _____

_____   _____

_____   _____

Meals
وجبات

Iftar
الإفطار

Suhoor
سحور

_____

_____

_____

_____

_____

Water Tracker
تعقب المياه

(1) (2) (3) (4) (5) (6) (7) (8)

Daily Reflection
تفكر و تدبر

How did my day go? What is a blessing I am thankful for today?

_____

_____

_____

_____

_____

_____

_____

_____

_____

Sudoku #8

1			3	8	2		6	4
	8	4	7					
2		5					8	7
9		6		7		8	4	2
4		2						
8	1	3	4	2	5			9
7	2	9	8	3			1	
5	6						9	
								6

رمضان 25

Date/ خيرات: ـــــــــــــــــ

○ Fajr   صلاة الفجر   ○ Dhuhr   صَلَاة الظهر

○ Asr   صلاة العصر   ○ Maghrib   صلاة المغرب

○ Isha'a   صلاة العشاء   ○ Taraweeh   تراويح

○ Reading completed for today   اكتملت القراءة لهذا اليوم

Ayaah/Hadith for Today
آية/ حديث اليوم

_____

_____

_____

My Goals
أهدافي

Things to Do
الأشياء الذي ينبغي فعلها

_____

_____

_____

My Good Deeds
أعمالي الصالحة

_____

_____

_____

_____

Meals
وجبات

Iftar
الإفطار

_____

_____

_____

_____

_____

Suhoor
سحور

_____

_____

_____

_____

_____

Water Tracker
تعقب المياه

(1) (2) (3) (4) (5) (6) (7) (8)

Daily Reflection
تفكر و تدبر

How did my day go? What progress did I make towards my goals?

_____

_____

_____

_____

_____

_____

_____

_____

_____

رمضان 26

Date/ خيرات: ـــــــــــــــــــــــ

- ◯ Fajr — صلاة الفجر
- ◯ Asr — صلاة العصر
- ◯ Isha'a — صلاة العشاء
- ◯ Reading completed for today — اكتملت القراءة لهذا اليوم

- ◯ Dhuhr — صَلَاة الظهر
- ◯ Maghrib — صلاة المغرب
- ◯ Taraweeh — تراويح

Ayaah/Hadith for Today
آية/ حديث اليوم

_____

_____

_____

My Goals
أهدافي

_____

_____

My Good Deeds
أعمالي الصالحة

_____

_____

_____

Things to Do
الأشياء الذي ينبغي فعلها

_____

_____

_____

_____

_____

_____

_____

Meals
وجبات

Iftar
الإفطار

Suhoor
سحور

_____
_____
_____
_____
_____

_____
_____
_____
_____
_____

Water Tracker
تعقب المياه

(1) (2) (3) (4) (5) (6) (7) (8)

Daily Reflection
تفكر و تدبر

How did my day go? What is one thing I did better today? How does that make me feel?

_____
_____
_____
_____
_____
_____
_____
_____
_____

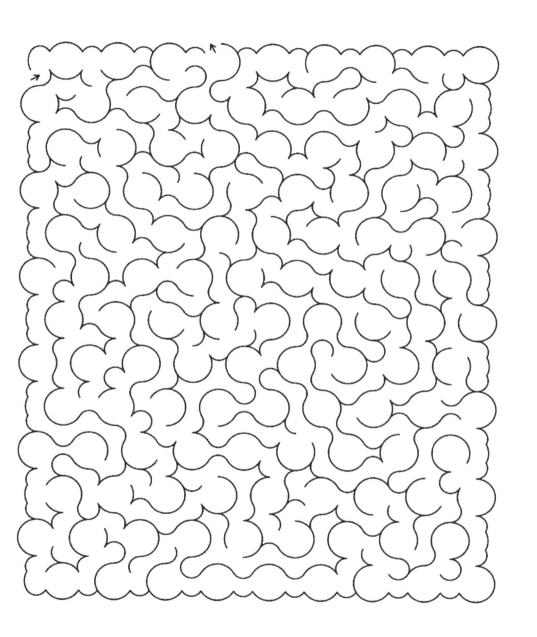

رمضان 27

Date/ خيرات: ــــــــــــــــــــــــ

- ⬭ Fajr — صلاة الفجر
- ⬭ Asr — صلاة العصر
- ⬭ Isha'a — صلاة العشاء
- ⬭ Reading completed for today — اكتملت القراءة لهذا اليوم

- ⬭ Dhuhr — صَلَاة الظهر
- ⬭ Maghrib — صلاة المغرب
- ⬭ Taraweeh — تراويح

Ayaah/Hadith for Today
آية/ حديث اليوم

ــ

ــ

ــ

My Goals
أهدافي

ــــــــــــــــــــــــــــــــ

ــــــــــــــــــــــــــــــــ

ــــــــــــــــــــــــــــــــ

My Good Deeds
أعمالي الصالحة

ــــــــــــــــــــــــــــــــ

ــــــــــــــــــــــــــــــــ

ــــــــــــــــــــــــــــــــ

Things to Do
الأشياء الذي ينبغي فعلها

ــــــــــــــــــــــــــــــــ

ــــــــــــــــــــــــــــــــ

ــــــــــــــــــــــــــــــــ

ــــــــــــــــــــــــــــــــ

ــــــــــــــــــــــــــــــــ

ــــــــــــــــــــــــــــــــ

Meals
وجبات

Iftar
الإفطار

Suhoor
سحور

_____   _____

_____   _____

_____   _____

_____   _____

_____   _____

Water Tracker
تعقب المياه

(1) (2) (3) (4) (5) (6) (7) (8)

Daily Reflection
تفكر و تدبر

How did my day go? What is one thing I can do better tomorrow? How can I do that?

_____

_____

_____

_____

_____

_____

_____

_____

_____

_____

رمضان 28

Date/ خيرات: _____

- ◯ Fajr — صلاة الفجر
- ◯ Asr — صلاة العصر
- ◯ Isha'a — صلاة العشاء
- ◯ Reading completed for today — اكتملت القراءة لهذا اليوم

- ◯ Dhuhr — صَلَاة الظهر
- ◯ Maghrib — صلاة المغرب
- ◯ Taraweeh — تراويح

Ayaah/Hadith for Today
آية/ حديث اليوم

_____
_____
_____

My Goals
أهدافي

_____
_____
_____

My Good Deeds
أعمالي الصالحة

_____
_____
_____

Things to Do
الأشياء الذي ينبغي فعلها

_____
_____
_____
_____
_____
_____
_____

Meals
وجبات

Iftar
الإفطار

Suhoor
سحور

_____
_____
_____
_____
_____

_____
_____
_____
_____
_____

Water Tracker
تعقب المياه

(1) (2) (3) (4) (5) (6) (7) (8)

Daily Reflection
تفكر و تدبر

How did my day go? What is a special moment I want to remember from today?

_____
_____
_____
_____
_____
_____
_____
_____
_____

Sudoku #9

	5				9		1	3
3		2	6		1	8		5
		7					6	
	2				4	6		
4	8			9	6			
9		6		2	8	4	3	1
	3	5	1		2			
		4	9	3		1	5	8
7		9						

رمضان 29

Date/ خيرات: _____

- ◯ Fajr — صلاة الفجر
- ◯ Asr — صلاة العصر
- ◯ Isha'a — صلاة العشاء
- ◯ Dhuhr — صَلَاة الظهر
- ◯ Maghrib — صلاة المغرب
- ◯ Taraweeh — تراويح
- ◯ Reading completed for today — اكتملت القراءة لهذا اليوم

Ayaah/Hadith for Today
آية/ حديث اليوم

_____

_____

_____

My Goals
أهدافي

_____

_____

_____

My Good Deeds
أعمالي الصالحة

_____

_____

_____

Things to Do
الأشياء الذي ينبغي فعلها

_____

_____

_____

_____

_____

_____

_____

Meals
وجبات

Iftar
الإفطار

_____

_____

_____

_____

_____

Suhoor
سحور

_____

_____

_____

_____

_____

Water Tracker
تعقب المياه

(1) (2) (3) (4) (5) (6) (7) (8)

Daily Reflection
تفكر و تدبر

How did my day go? What is a blessing I am thankful for today?

_____

_____

_____

_____

_____

_____

_____

_____

_____

رمضان 30

Date/ خيرات: _____

⬤ Fajr	صلاة الفجر	⬤ Dhuhr	صَلَاة الظهر
⬤ Asr	صلاة العصر	⬤ Maghrib	صلاة المغرب
⬤ Isha'a	صلاة العشاء	⬤ Taraweeh	تراويح

⬤ Reading completed for today   اكتملت القراءة لهذا اليوم

Ayaah/Hadith for Today
آية/ حديث اليوم

_____
_____
_____

My Goals
أهدافي

Things to Do
الأشياء الذي ينبغي فعلها

_____   _____
_____   _____
_____   _____

My Good Deeds
أعمالي الصالحة

_____   _____
_____   _____
_____   _____
_____   _____

Meals
وجبات

Iftar
الإفطار

Suhoor
سحور

_____   _____
_____   _____
_____   _____
_____   _____
_____   _____

Water Tracker
تعقب المياه

(1) (2) (3) (4) (5) (6) (7) (8)

Daily Reflection
تفكر و تدبر

How did my day go? What are 3 things I want to remember about this month?

_____
_____
_____
_____
_____
_____
_____
_____

Sudoku #10

1			9			7		8
					8	9	3	6
				4			5	2
6		1				5		7
	9		5	1	7		6	
7		4	8		3	2	1	
	4				1		9	5
	2					3		1
				8	9		2	

Notes

Sudoku Answers

Sudoku #1

3	7	4	1	8	6	2	5	9
2	1	9	5	4	7	8	6	3
6	8	5	3	2	9	1	4	7
5	4	7	9	6	8	3	2	1
9	2	1	7	3	5	4	8	6
8	6	3	2	1	4	7	9	5
1	5	2	4	9	3	6	7	8
4	9	8	6	7	1	5	3	2
7	3	6	8	5	2	9	1	4

Sudoku #2

5	6	4	8	3	7	1	2	9
9	2	7	6	1	4	5	3	8
1	3	8	2	5	9	6	7	4
3	4	1	7	6	8	2	9	5
8	7	6	9	2	5	4	1	3
2	9	5	1	4	3	8	6	7
4	8	2	3	7	6	9	5	1
7	1	9	5	8	2	3	4	6
6	5	3	4	9	1	7	8	2

Sudoku #3

3	8	7	4	1	6	2	5	9
9	4	2	3	7	5	1	8	6
6	1	5	2	9	8	7	3	4
1	7	8	6	4	3	9	2	5
5	6	4	8	2	9	3	1	7
2	9	3	1	5	7	4	6	8
8	2	9	5	3	4	6	7	1
4	3	6	7	8	1	5	9	2
7	5	1	9	6	2	8	4	3

Sudoku #4

1	2	8	5	7	3	9	4	6
7	4	5	9	8	6	2	3	1
9	3	6	4	2	1	8	7	5
5	1	2	7	3	9	6	8	4
4	7	9	8	6	5	3	1	2
6	8	3	2	1	4	7	5	9
2	9	7	1	4	8	5	6	3
3	5	1	6	9	7	4	2	8
8	6	4	3	5	2	1	9	7

Sudoku Answers

Sudoku #5

5	6	7	2	1	9	8	4	3
2	1	3	4	5	8	6	9	7
4	8	9	6	7	3	1	2	5
8	5	2	3	9	7	4	6	1
3	9	1	5	4	6	7	8	2
6	7	4	1	8	2	3	5	9
9	4	6	7	2	1	5	3	8
1	2	5	8	3	4	9	7	6
7	3	8	9	6	5	2	1	4

Sudoku #6

8	7	4	6	3	1	9	2	5
5	3	6	8	2	9	4	7	1
9	2	1	4	5	7	3	6	8
4	1	5	7	8	6	2	9	3
6	9	2	5	4	3	1	8	7
7	8	3	1	9	2	5	4	6
3	4	7	2	6	5	8	1	9
1	5	8	9	7	4	6	3	2
2	6	9	3	1	8	7	5	4

Sudoku #7

2	9	3	6	8	7	1	5	4
4	5	1	3	9	2	6	8	7
7	8	6	5	1	4	3	9	2
3	1	8	2	4	5	9	7	6
6	2	9	7	3	1	5	4	8
5	4	7	8	6	9	2	3	1
1	3	2	9	7	8	4	6	5
9	7	5	4	2	6	8	1	3
8	6	4	1	5	3	7	2	9

Sudoku #8

1	9	7	3	8	2	5	6	4
6	8	4	7	5	9	2	3	1
2	3	5	6	1	4	9	8	7
9	5	6	1	7	3	8	4	2
4	7	2	9	6	8	1	5	3
8	1	3	4	2	5	6	7	9
7	2	9	8	3	6	4	1	5
5	6	1	2	4	7	3	9	8
3	4	8	5	9	1	7	2	6

Sudoku Answers

Sudoku #9

6	5	8	2	4	9	7	1	3
3	4	2	6	7	1	8	9	5
1	9	7	8	5	3	2	6	4
5	2	3	7	1	4	6	8	9
4	8	1	3	9	6	5	7	2
9	7	6	5	2	8	4	3	1
8	3	5	1	6	2	9	4	7
2	6	4	9	3	7	1	5	8
7	1	9	4	8	5	3	2	6

Sudoku #10

1	6	2	9	3	5	7	4	8
4	7	5	1	2	8	9	3	6
9	8	3	7	4	6	1	5	2
6	3	1	4	9	2	5	8	7
2	9	8	5	1	7	4	6	3
7	5	4	8	6	3	2	1	9
3	4	6	2	7	1	8	9	5
8	2	9	6	5	4	3	7	1
5	1	7	3	8	9	6	2	4

Made in the USA
Las Vegas, NV
28 March 2022

46446821R00066